GIRLZ ROCK!

Newspaper Scoop

Jacqueline Arena

illustrated by
Lloyd Foye

First published in 2006 by
MACMILLAN EDUCATION AUSTRALIA PTY LTD
627 Chapel Street, South Yarra, Australia 3141

Copyright © Felice Arena, Phil Kettle, and Jacqueline Arena 2006

This edition first published in the United States of America
in 2006 by MONDO Publishing.

All rights reserved.
No part of this publication may be reproduced, except in the case of
quotation for articles or reviews, or stored in any retrieval system, or
transmitted in any form or by any means, electronic, mechanical,
photocopying, recording, or otherwise, without written permission
from the publisher.

For information contact:
MONDO Publishing
980 Avenue of the Americas
New York, NY 10018

Visit our web site at http://www.mondopub.com

06 07 08 09 10   9 8 7 6 5 4 3 2 1

ISBN 1-59336-941-7 (PB)

Series created by Felice Arena and Phil Kettle
Project Management by Limelight Press Pty Ltd
Cover and text design by Lore Foye
Illustrations by Lloyd Foye

Printed in Hong Kong

GIRLZ ROCK!
Contents

CHAPTER 1
Write On! 1

CHAPTER 2
Sniffing Out a Story 8

CHAPTER 3
Spicy Rock Stars 15

CHAPTER 4
Secret Agent Possum 21

CHAPTER 5
The Big Poop...err, Scoop 25

EXTRA STUFF

• Newspaper Lingo 33

• Newspaper Musts 34

• Newspaper Instant Info 36

• Think Tank 38

• Hey, Girls! (Author Letter) 40

• When We Were Kids 42

• What a Laugh! 43

Rachel   Ellie

CHAPTER 1

Write On!

Ellie is in the schoolyard on her hands and knees, pointing a camera at the ground. She has a pad and pencil by her side. Her best friend Rachel runs over to her.

Rachel "Hey, El, what are you doing?"

Ellie "I'm looking at these ants."

Rachel "Why?"

Ellie "I've been asked to be a junior reporter for the school newspaper, and I want to write the best story ever."

Rachel "Oh, cool. Can I help?"

Ellie gets back up onto her feet.

Ellie "Um, well..."

Rachel "What? I can't help?"

Ellie "It's not that you can't help, it's..."

Rachel "Look El, I know you're a better writer than me, but I can do other things like, um..."

Ellie "I know! You can be my photographer."

Rachel "What? And take photos?"

Ellie "Yeah."

Ellie takes off the camera and hangs it around Rachel's neck.

Rachel "Okay, great. I was gonna say I'd help you come up with better stories, but this is cool."

Ellie "Come up with better stories? What's wrong with writing about all the different types of ants?"

Rachel "Bor-ing! Major snooze-fest! Unless…"

Ellie "Unless what?"

Rachel "Unless you write about killer ants the size of ponies that march into school and start eating all the desks and chairs in the classrooms."

Ellie "I can't write that! It's not true."

Rachel "But it's more exciting."

Ellie "Yeah, but the readers need to know the truth. That's what newspapers are all about."

Rachel "Fine. If it's a true story you want, I've got the perfect one—and it'll be a really big poop!"

Ellie "You mean 'scoop.' That's a story that no one has ever written about before. Something that'll be big news to everyone."

Rachel "Yeah, yeah...poop, scoop—whatever."

Ellie "So, what's the big scoop?"

Rachel "You'll see. Follow me and I'll lead you to the source."

Ellie "Right, chief. I'm on the case."

CHAPTER 2

Sniffing Out a Story

Ellie follows Rachel across the schoolyard.

Ellie "Rach, where are we going?"

Rachel "You'll see. This is gonna be front page news."

Ellie "I can't wait!"

Rachel sneaks up toward the staff room window.

Ellie "Rach, why are we spying on the teachers?"

Rachel "*Shhh*! Don't let 'em see us."

Rachel and Ellie hide behind some bushes and peek into the staff room.

Ellie (whispering) "What are we
 looking at?"

Rachel "There's your big scoop, El."

Ellie takes a closer look at the
teachers in the staff room.

Ellie "What scoop? They're just
 eating and talking."

Rachel "No, look closer!"

Ellie "The only news I can see around here is that Miss Taylor has her hair up today when she usually wears it down."

Rachel "El, how can that be news? That's like saying that birds fly in the sky or polar bears love ice."

Ellie "I guess."

Rachel "But it'd be huge news if it was something like, birds like to drive sports cars or polar bears love to rollerblade."

Ellie "Okay, okay, I get it. So, what's the big scoop?"

Rachel "Look at Mr. Rogers. He's sitting next to Miss Ferrini. And if you look closer, he's holding her hand."

Ellie "So?"

Rachel "El, that's the scoop!
Mr. Rogers is in love with Miss
Ferrini! Now, if we can only get a
picture of them smooching, it'll be
front page news!"

Ellie "That's not news. Everyone
knows that they're in love. They've
been all gooey with each other
for a long time."

Rachel "They have?"

Ellie "Yeah, and they told everyone at assembly last week that they're engaged. You were out sick that day."

Ellie gives a sigh then walks off.

Rachel "Where are you going?"
Ellie "To the cafeteria. Maybe I can find a story there."

CHAPTER 3

Spicy Rock Stars

Ellie returns to Rachel after talking to the cafeteria ladies about some possible story ideas.

Rachel "So, any big news happening there?"

Ellie "Well, they've run out of red apples, but they've still got plenty of green ones."

Rachel "Bor-ing!"

Ellie "What about promoting the yogurt of the week?"

Rachel "I don't think so!"

Ellie "Or how they've started selling hot and spicy chips?"

Rachel "Mega bor-ing!"

Ellie "Yeah, you're right."

Rachel "Unless..."

Ellie "Unless what?"

Rachel "Unless you write about the canteen's hot and spicy apples— how when you bite into them, steam comes out of your ears."

Ellie shakes her head.

Ellie "I wanna write about something real, Rach—like an actual reporter."

Rachel "If I were a reporter, I'd wanna be a music reporter. I'd interview all the great rock stars. They'd get me up on stage and everyone'd be screaming, *'Rachel! Rachel! You're too cool to be a reporter! You should be a rock star and...'*"

Rachel gets so carried away that at first she doesn't notice Ellie running off.

Rachel "Now where's she going?"

Ellie heads toward a group of kids who are all huddled together. Rachel runs after her.

Rachel "Wait up, El!"

Rachel catches up with Ellie.

Rachel "What's going on? What's everyone looking at?"

Ellie "That's what I'm trying to find out. Whatever it is, it could be big news."

CHAPTER 4

Secret Agent Possum

Ellie and Rachel push themselves
to the front of the group to see what
everyone is looking at.

Rachel "Eww, gross!"
Ellie "That's disgusting!"

Everyone is crowded around a dead opossum. Some of the boys even try to pick it up—until the school's groundsman comes and takes it away. Ellie and Rachel go and sit under a tree.

Ellie "I guess I can write about that."
Rachel "And say what?"
Ellie "That it was an old opossum and it just died."

Ellie catches Rachel rolling her eyes.

Ellie "I know what you're gonna
say—bor-ing!"
Rachel "Well, it would be unless…"

This time Ellie rolls her eyes.

Ellie (sighs) "Unless what?"

Rachel "Unless you write that it was a secret agent opossum on a mission looking for red apples, but that it died of shock when it saw..."

Ellie "Rach!"

Rachel "Okay, I'll stop. But what are you going to write about then?"

CHAPTER 5

The Big Poop...err, Scoop

Suddenly, a white, wet, gooey drop falls from the branches above onto Ellie's head. Ellie feels her hair with her hand.

Ellie "Eww, yuck! A bird just pooped on me!"

Ellie looks up to see a nest full of chicks.

Ellie "I don't believe it. Look, Rach!"

Rachel "Are they magpie chicks?"

Ellie "No, better. This is huge news! They're owls!"

Rachel "Owls? Wow, that's so cool!"

Ellie "Rach, can you take a photo?"

Rachel "Sure, how about a close-up?"

Rachel begins to climb the tree.

Ellie "Rach! What are you doing?
I meant take a photo from down
here."

But it's too late. Rachel is already
halfway up the tree. She starts
climbing toward the owls' nest.

Ellie "Hey, Rach, can you get a real close-up of the babies? They're so cute, they'll make a great feature!"

Rachel "I'm trying to get out to that branch. If I can get a little closer, I know I'll get the best shot ever."

Rachel inches her way along the branch.

Ellie "Be careful, Rach!"

Rachel "I will. Just tell me if you see the mother anywhere. I don't want to be attacked."

Ellie "Okay. This is gonna be the *best* newspaper story!"

Rachel takes a photo of the owl chicks in their nest. She scampers back down the tree.

Ellie "Tell me what you saw so I can write about it."

Rachel "Well, one was green and slimy. The other one had four eyes and looked like a lizard with wings."

Ellie "What?"

Rachel "Just joking. They were amazing, El."

Ellie "Let me take a look."

Rachel "See? On the screen?"

Ellie "Wow! They're awesome! So cute! The story's flooding into my head right now. I've gotta go to the library and write it all down."

Two days later, the school newspaper comes out. Everyone congratulates Ellie and Rachel on a great story.

Ellie "Thanks, Rach."

Rachel "For what?"

Ellie "For helping me find something exciting to write about."

Rachel "It was nothing. You were the one who ended up getting the big scoop—and the big bird poop!"

Rachel

GIRLZROCK!
Newspaper Lingo

Ellie

editor The head of a newspaper; the person who decides what stories will appear in the paper.

headline The title of a newspaper article. The words are usually short and snappy, and the letters are in really large print.

paperboy or papergirl A boy or girl who delivers newspapers to people's homes—not paper doll cutouts!

reporter Also called a journalist, a reporter tells or writes about the news.

scoop The story kind—not the ice cream kind! A scoop is a big news story, one that will sell tons of newspapers.

GIRLZ ROCK!
Newspaper Musts

☆ If you want to be a reporter, grab a pen and notepad and go interview someone, like maybe a grandparent or teacher. Then write a story about him or her and send it in to your local paper. They might just print it!

☆ Check out the pull-out sections for kids in the newspapers—weekend editions usually have them. You'll find quizzes, games, and other cool stuff—written just for you!

☆ Don't throw out old newspapers. They can be used to wrap things up or to line the bottom of a bird or hamster cage.

☆ Read a newspaper article and then bring it up at the dinner table. Your parents will be really impressed when you say something like, "So, I read that the price of gas will be going up this summer!"

☆ Always carry a camera with you. You never know when you might come across a great scoop, and you'll want to be sure to get a photo of it.

☆ Instead of using your real first name, sign the news stories you write with a cool reporter's name, like "Scoop" or "Flash."

GIRLZ ROCK!

Newspaper Instant Info

The oldest weekend newspaper is the *Observer*, published in the United Kingdom. Its first issue came out on December 4, 1791.

On average, the *New York Times* is read by 1,094,000 people from Monday through Friday and by 1,650,000 people on Sundays.

The highest honor a journalist can receive is being awarded a Pulitzer Prize. Pulitzers are awarded to the best news reports of the year.

Most newspaper sports pages are in the back of the paper.

The heaviest newspaper edition ever was the September 14, 1987 edition of the Sunday *New York Times.* It weighed almost 12 pounds (5.4 kilograms) and had 1,612 pages.

Clark Kent, better known as Superman, worked as a reporter for a newspaper called the *Daily Planet.*

There are over 10,000 newspapers available on the Internet. Now that's saving a lot of trees from being cut down!

The first regularly published newspaper in America was a weekly paper published in Boston beginning in 1704. The paper was only one page long.

GIRLZROCK!
Think Tank

1 What does Rachel think will be a big scoop for Ellie and the school paper?

2 What do Ellie and Rachel find up in the tree that turns out to be a big story?

3 How does Rachel get a close-up photo of the owl babies?

4 Which superhero worked as a reporter at a daily newspaper?

5 What's a headline?

6 Do you think it's okay that Ellie and Rachel peek into the teacher's room because they are trying to get a scoop for the paper? Why or why not?

7 Do you think Rachel should have climbed the tree in order to get a close-up photo of the owl babies? Why or why not?

8 Should news reporters be able to put made-up information in their stories? Explain your answer.

Answers

1. Rachel thinks that two teachers holding hands will be a big news scoop.
2. Ellie and Rachel find a nest of owl babies up in the tree.
3. Rachel climbs the tree in order to get a close-up photo of the owl babies.
4. Superman worked as a reporter at the *Daily Planet*.
5. A headline is the main title of a newspaper story.
6. Answers will vary.
7. Answers will vary.
8. Answers will vary.

How did you score?

- If you got most of the answers correct, you should definitely consider becoming a reporter for your school newspaper.

- If you got more than half of the answers correct, then you probably enjoy reading the kids' section of the newspaper.

- If you got less than half of the answers correct, then you love newspapers— but only to line the bottom of your canary's cage!

Hey, Girls!

I hope that you have as much fun reading my story as I have had writing it. I loved reading and writing stories when I was young.

Here are some suggestions that might help you enjoy reading even more than you do now.

At school, why don't you use "Newspaper Scoop" as a play, and you and your friends can be the actors. Get some old newspapers, a pad, a pencil, and a camera to use as props. So...have you decided who is going to be Ellie and who is going to be Rachel? And what about the narrator?

Now, act out the story in front of your friends. I'm sure you'll have a great time!

You also might like to take this story home and get someone in your family to read it with you. Maybe they can take on a part in the story.

Whatever you choose to do, you can have as much fun with reading and writing as a polar bear has in a freezer!

And remember, Girlz Rock!

Jacqueline Saena

GIRLZ ROCK!
When We Were Kids

Jacqueline *Shey*

Jacqueline talked to Shey, another *Girlz Rock!* author

Jacqueline "Have you ever been in the newspaper?"

Shey "Yeah, when I was younger."

Jacqueline "It must've have been exciting to see yourself in print."

Shey "Well, it was for my mom and dad. Everyone said I looked great."

Jacqueline "So why weren't you excited?"

Shey "'Because I was busy gurgling."

Jacqueline "Gurgling?"

Shey "Yeah, it was a photo of me on the day I was born!"

What a Laugh!

Q What books do owls like?

A Hoot-dunits!